Meet ...
everyone from

This is the **Furious Five**. They are Po's friends. They are kung fu fighters. They live in the **Valley of Peace**.

Crane

Mantis

Monkey

Viper

Tigress

Po is the Dragon Warrior. He is very good at kung fu.

Li lost his son a long time ago. He lives in the Panda Village.

Master Shifu is Po's teacher and a kung fu master. He lives at the Jade Palace.

Po

Li Shan

Master Shifu

This is the **Panda Village**. Lots of pandas live there.

Panda Village

Master Oogway and Kai live in the **Spirit World**.

The Spirit World

Master Oogway knows a lot of things.

Master Oogway

Kai

Jombies

Kai controls the green **jombies**.

Before you read ...
What do you think?
Are Kai and Master Oogway friends?

3

New Words

What do these new words mean? Ask your teacher or use your dictionary.

destroy

They are **destroying** the house.

attack

The dog is **attacking** the girl.

fight

The girls are **fighting**. They are good fighters.

control

He is **controlling** the car.

hurt

Her foot **hurts**.

lose

She can't find her shoe. Her shoe is **lost**.

power

This car has electric **power**.

son

They have three **sons**.

student

There are only four **students** in his class.

teach

She is **teaching** the children.

'It's your turn'

It's your **turn**!

Verbs

Present	Past
fight	fought
lose	lost
take	took

CHAPTER ONE
Master Shifu's last class

Po and the Furious Five ran to the Jade Palace for their kung fu class. Master Shifu was there.

'Hello, students,' he said. 'Today is my last class.'

Everyone stopped. 'Why?' they asked.

'Because Po is going to be your teacher.'

'Why me?' asked Po.

'Because you're the Dragon Warrior. It's your turn.'

Po was not happy. 'How can I teach the Furious Five?' he thought.

'OK, Tigress, jump up!' he said. 'Now, Crane fly down! And Monkey, stand and fight!'

Bang! Crash! Everyone fell down.

'This is no good!' said Po's friends.

'I'm not a good teacher,' said Po sadly.

Po talked to Master Shifu.

'I don't want to teach,' said Po. 'I want to fight.'

'I can't teach you now,' answered Master Shifu. 'I must learn about chi.'

'What's chi?' asked Po.

'Chi is the power in everything that lives,' answered Master Shifu and he walked away.

CHAPTER TWO
A new panda in town

'I don't understand chi,' thought Po.

He went to town to think.

'Look Po, there's a new panda here,' said his friends. 'He can eat more than you!'

'More than me?' answered Po. 'Where is he?'

Then Po saw a very big panda at the table.

'Who are you?' Po asked.

'I'm Li Shan. I'm looking for my son. I lost him when he was a baby.'

'I lost my father,' answered Po.

Li looked at Po. Po looked at Li.

'Dad!' said Po.

'Son!' said Li.

Po was very happy. He and his panda father talked and talked. Po learned a lot.

'Are there more pandas?' Po asked.

'Yes,' answered Li. 'We all live together in the Panda Village. It's a beautiful place.'

'Let's go to my school at the Jade Palace,' said Po. 'It's cool!'

CHAPTER 3
'Who is Kai?'

Po and Li were at the Jade Palace when suddenly some terrible green animals attacked. They were jombies.

'I am Kai,' said the jombies all at the same time. Kai was speaking through the jombies. 'My jombies are going to take your chi.'

But Po, Master Shifu and the Furious Five fought them and the jombies went away.

'Kai controls the jombies,' said Po. 'But who is Kai?'

Po and his friends went to the Jade Palace. Master Shifu opened an old book.

'My teacher, Master Oogway, wrote this book before he went to the Spirit World. Maybe we can find out who Kai is. Let's read it.'

A long time ago, when I was young, Kai was my friend...

One day I was hurt but Kai took me to the Panda Village. The pandas helped me with their chi. But Kai saw the power of chi and he started to take it from the pandas. I fought Kai and I put him in the Spirit World. But if he comes from the Spirit World again only a master of chi can stop him.

'I must learn about chi,' said Po.

'Come to the Panda Village,' said Li. 'Pandas know a lot about chi. I can teach you. You can learn to live, eat and sleep like the other pandas.'

'Wow! That's exciting,' said Po. 'Yes, let's go!'

CHAPTER 4
The Panda Village

Po went to the Panda Village with Li. It was a very beautiful place.

There were a lot of other pandas. Bao loved to play games. Mei Mei loved to dance. Dim and Sum loved to jump. Po was very happy to meet his new friends and family.

Back in the Valley of Peace, Master Shifu and the Furious Five had terrible problems.

Kai came and he destroyed the Jade Palace. He fought with some of the Furious Five and he took their chi. Now they were green jombies.

Kai saw Master Shifu. 'Now it's your turn. I'm going to take your chi,' he said. 'You can't stop me!'

'Someone is going to stop you one day,' answered Master Shifu.

'Who can stop me? The panda?' shouted Kai. 'My chi is stronger.'

He fought with Master Shifu and took his chi. Master Shifu was a jombie now too.

'Now I'm going to destroy the Panda Village,' said Kai.

But Tigress saw everything. 'I must tell Po,' she thought.

Tigress went to the Panda Village.

'Kai is coming,' she said to the pandas. 'He wants to destroy everything and take everyone's chi.'

She looked at Po. 'You must stop him. Do you know all about chi now?'

'No...' answered Po. 'I don't.'

'Dad,' said Po to Li. 'You must teach me about chi now!'

'I can't,' answered Li. 'I don't know anything about chi.'

'What?' said Po. 'But you said ...'

Li was sad. 'I'm sorry,' he said. 'I was frightened for you. I didn't want to lose you again. It was dangerous for you to stay in the Valley of Peace.'

CHAPTER 5
The power of chi

Po was angry with his dad, Li. 'What can I do?' thought Po.

'We are all pandas,' said his friends and family. 'We can all fight Kai. You can teach us.'

'Yes, now it's your turn!' answered Po. 'Bao is good at playing games. Dim and Sum are good at jumping. Mei Mei can dance. I can help you all to be the best!'

The pandas learned a lot from Po. When Kai came to the Panda Village with his jombies, the pandas were waiting. They fought the jombies well.

Then Kai saw Po. 'Now it's your turn,' Kai said. 'I'm going to take your chi.'

Po and Kai fought but Kai was very strong.

Kai started to take Po's chi. 'It's the end for you, panda!' he said.

'We need to help Po!' said Li. 'Let's all give him our chi.'

The pandas all thought hard. The power of their chi went to Po.

'I can stop you now!' said Po to Kai. He fought with Kai again.

'Aaaaarrr!' shouted Kai. 'You are too strong for me now.'

Po destroyed Kai's chi.

'Kai is back in the Spirit World. He can't hurt us now,' said Po to everyone.

The pandas were all very happy.

'You are a master of chi now,' said Li.

'Yes, now I understand chi,' said Po. 'You all gave me your chi and then I was strong. That's panda power!'

THE END

KUNG FU

Kung fu is very old. It started in China about 4,000 years ago.

The Shaolin Temple

The Shaolin Temple was a very important place for kung fu teachers more than 1,000 years ago.

A student of kung fu learns about chi, the power in all things.

It is important to control your chi.

★
Would you like to learn kung fu? Why / Why not?
★

Answers a: crane **b:** monkey **c:** mantis **d:** snake **e:** tiger

Kung fu animals

When you do kung fu, you move like different animals.

Look at these pictures of the tiger, crane, snake, monkey and mantis moves.

Can you name each animal?

Did you know?

Kung fu means to learn something by hard work.

功夫

A kung fu master looks for peace and control of his or her mind and body.

Belts

The colour of a student's belt is important in kung fu. Many students of kung fu start with a **white** belt.

Yellow, **orange** and **blue** belts – you are getting better at kung fu.

Green, **brown** and **red** belts belts – you are good at kung fu.

Black belt – you are very good at kung fu and you can teach it.

What do these words mean? Find out.

belt   body   mind   peace

After you read

1 True (✓) or False (✗)? Write in the box.

a) Po doesn't teach the Furious Five very well. ✓

b) Chi is a panda. ☐

c) Li Shan can eat more than Po. ☐

d) Li Shan lives in the Valley of Peace. ☐

e) Kai was Oogway's friend. ☐

f) Po didn't like the Panda Village. ☐

g) Master Shifu took Kai's chi. ☐

h) The pandas helped Po with their chi. ☐

2 Write the correct name.

**Oogway   Tigress   Kai
Li Shan   ~~Master Shifu~~**

a) It was his last class.   Master Shifu
....

b) He lost his son.   ....

c) He was Master Shifu's teacher.   ....

d) He controlled the jombies.   ....

e) She saw Kai taking Master Shifu's chi.   ....

Where's the popcorn?
Look in your book.
Can you find it?

Puzzle time!

1 Complete the sentences. Put the verbs in the correct form.

teach   eat   dance   fight   ~~jump~~

a) Two pandas are   jumping. ....

b) Four pandas are   ....

c) One panda is   ....

d) Five pandas are   ....

e) Three pandas are   ....

2 Circle the verbs and match present and past tenses.

go lose think give fight take

fought lost thought took gave went

3 Look and match.

 **1** d

 **2**

 **3**

 **4**

a) Po helped the pandas do kung fu.

b) Po fought Kai.

c) Po went to the Panda Village.

d) Po found his panda dad, Li.

4 Draw your favourite part of the story. What are the characters doing? How are they feeling?

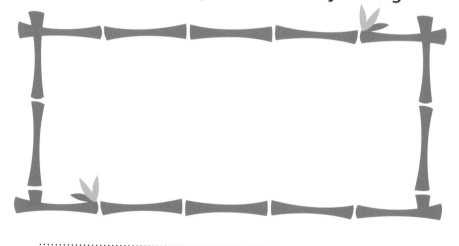

....

....

....

Imagine...

Work with a friend. Act out the scenes.

A

Po	I don't want to teach. I want to fight.
Master Shifu	I can't teach you now. I must learn about chi.
Po	What's chi?
Master Shifu	Chi is the power in everything that lives.

B

Po	Who are you?
Li Shan	I'm Li Shan. I'm looking for my son. I lost him when he was a baby.
Po	I lost my father. ... Dad!
Li Shan	Son!

Chant

1 🎧 Listen and read.

The power of chi

Panda power is
The power of chi.
The power in you,
The power in me.

I give it to you,
You give it to me.
That's panda power,
The power of chi.

The power to learn,
The power to know.
That's panda power,
The power of Po!

2 🎧 Say the chant.